CONNECTED LEADERSHIP JOURNAL

Exploring Your Leader P.O.V.®

James P. Sartain, Jr., Ph.D.
Kathryn W. Davanzo, M.Ed.

Second Edition

Connected Leadership Journal

Exploring Your Leader P.O.V.®

Second Edition

ISBN-10:   0985030305
ISBN-13:   978-0-9850303-0-8

Published by CODA Partners, Inc., Learning Products Division, Tampa, Florida

Printed in the United States

Request for information should be addressed to:
CODA Partners, Inc.
Pasco Florida Office
37322 Meridian Avenue, Dade City, FL 33525
http://www.codapartners.net

Library of Congress Cataloging-in-Publication Data
Sartain, James P.
Leader P.O.V.™ Journal: Exploring Your Leader P.O.V.
James P. Sartain, Jr. & Kathryn W. Davanzo – 2nd ed.
    1. Leadership 2. Performance. 3. Leadership Identity.

Connected Leadership Journal

Exploring Your Leader P.O.V.®

Table of Contents

SECTION 1

Preface

Growing your skills, as a leader is a complex, multifaceted, and ongoing process of inquiry, discovery, application, and evaluation. It includes a large dose of trial and error, risk taking, and candid self-assessment. Connected Leadership is an evidence-based approach to leadership development that is supported by over twenty years of research with thousands of leaders. The approach has received extensive field-testing, having been applied in hundreds of individual, team, and organizational development programs and has consistently demonstrated positive and sustainable results. Why does it work? Because Connected Leadership is a comprehensive developmental approach that targets the cognitive elements of leadership—an emerging research focus that suggests the clarity of a leader's self-identity is one of the strongest predictors of leadership effectiveness.

A central focus of the Connected Leadership program is based in the power of reflective practice; looking inward and evaluating defining experiences, challenges, and opportunities and examining your leader self-identity. By applying a reflective practice, you can examine what you are learning and experiencing in a deliberate and purposeful way. Journaling is a proven reflective practice that helps you to retain information, better integrate new ideas and practices into daily work habits, and synthesize old learning with new learning. Most importantly, the activity of reflecting on key insights helps to clarify and strengthen your leader self-identity— which has been associated with leader emergence and performance.

You will begin with journal themes and topics that help clarify what you want to accomplish in leadership (your leadership intention). These themes and topics will be followed by questions written to help you clarify your leader self-identity. You will next reflect upon specific critical leader success skills, or super skills, known in our framework as "meta-competencies." Meta-competencies are those leadership skills found in research to be most associated with leader effectiveness and include examination, exploration, enlistment, and execution. This inside-out approach aligns intention, identity, and the core competencies to help you discover your unique pathway for maximizing your leadership potential and to write and articulate your personal leadership philosophy.

SECTION 2

Framework

CODA has devoted its leadership development practice to exploring how leaders become leaders and how leaders improve their leadership ability. This has led to an organizing framework for interventions with individuals, teams, and organizations. This framework is built on the premise that leaders are defined, first and foremost, by what they believe, what they know, how they seek what they do not know, and how they organize and lead others to achieve lasting business results.

Through CODA's research projects and 25+ years of working collaboratively as leaders both within and outside of organizations, we began to focus on what made some leaders effective and others ineffective. Through several years of interviews and observations, we noticed a common characteristic among the leaders identified as effective by their peers, supervisors, and staff. These leaders demonstrated a clarity and confidence in their identities as leaders. Their self-descriptions confirmed, time and again, that they did not hesitate or struggle when asked to describe their leadership approach and philosophy, their values, and their intentions. These effective leaders knew who they were and what they wanted to achieve.

Eventually, we felt compelled to rigorously research and test our observations. We analyzed years of leader interviews and observations through a grounded theory investigation. Through our research, we found specific elements related to self-identity, intention, and competencies that were common across effective leaders. These findings informed a theory of Connected Leadership and the resulting *Connected Leadership Framework*® (See Figure 1).

Our theory and model have been reinforced by the growing body of research by scholars interested in examining the link between a leader's self-identity and performance. Similarly, the specific meta-competencies identified in our framework have also been supported by a strong research base.

Today, we design all of CODA's individual, team, and organizational development initiatives to help strengthen leaders' intention, self-identity, and those success skills (leader meta-competencies) most associated with successful leadership.

Figure 1: Connected Leadership Framework®

Effective leaders:

- Have an understanding of what they want to accomplish and are driven to achieve their leadership purpose (**_Intention_**).

- See themselves as capable leaders, have positive self-appraisals about their leadership abilities, believe they can be successful in their leadership roles, and are consistent in their beliefs, behaviors, and values around leadership (**_Identity_**).

- Are acutely aware of theirs, and others, values, strengths, needs, and weaknesses, understand the social, political, and cultural contexts of the workplace and are able to leverage this awareness to maximize effective communication, relationships, business processes, and outcomes (**_Examination_**).

- Have a heightened sense of inquiry and actively explore industry and leadership best practices, challenge the status quo, and synthesize information into actionable strategies (**_Exploration_**).

- Define and cast a direction that resonates with their constituents, develop plans that align human resources, strategic objectives, and organizational processes, and maintain an appropriate sense of urgency throughout the course of a project or initiative (**_Enlistment_**).

- Are highly skilled in execution strategies and systems to help others prioritize, select, and follow through with the highest leverage actions. They relentlessly pursue results and foster accountability and follow through (**_Execution_**).

This journal is designed to help you explore each of these areas as you work to strengthen your leadership intention, clarify your leader self-identity, and articulate your Leader P.O.V.®, a highly personalized philosophy of leadership.

SECTION 3

Reflective Practice

By cultivating a process of continuous learning, reflection, and application, you increase your leadership effectiveness. You retain new learning and you integrate new concepts with existing concepts (known as inductive critical thinking) and your overall leadership competencies improve.

Reflective practice even helps you to identify distorted or inaccurate thinking that may be getting in your way. Simply put, when you learn something new, reflect upon its meaning and its connection to other knowledge, practices, and beliefs, and then attempt to apply it in real-world situations - your thinking improves and consequently, your ability to solve problems improves.

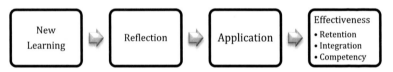

Our brains are comprised of "mental maps"—ingrained and well-traveled pathways that help us to process information quickly and efficiently. We train our brains to take short cuts by recognizing patterns and by subsequently pushing similar experiences into familiar categories. This increases the speed and efficiency of thought. But it comes at a price. This speed and efficiency limits the amount of new learning we can cull from new experiences, contributes to missing opportunities to be creative and innovative, and often allows us to continue to make the same mistakes over and over again. This journal will help you break from those patterns and to cultivate a new and more deliberate way of thinking.

Through this journey, you will be guided by questions and challenges designed to help you suspend assumptions and to expand your capacity as a leader through disciplined consideration of core themes and topics associated with effective leadership.

SECTION 4

Journaling Process

Remember this journal is for your eyes only. You can be candid and authentic with your beliefs, experiences, and opinions. Honest self-reflection is critical for you to obtain the most from this journal experience.

Many people go through life without a process of self-examination and as a result, are never aware of the untapped strengths they could leverage for greater success or an unchecked weakness that has created a barrier to leadership success.

The journal is organized into themes tied to *Connected Leadership Framework®*, with the addition of themes that link to leadership areas often found in the list of leader competencies that our clients expect their leaders to master.

The themes, and their subset topics and questions, will guide you as you reflect on the people, experiences, and contexts that have and will continue to shape your leadership. By giving honest thought to your responses you can refine what you believe in as a leader and who you are as a leader.

If you are using this journal in concert with a Connected Leadership Program or as part of a formal coaching process, your facilitator or coach will provide guidance on which themes, topics, and questions you should journal on during a designated time period. If you are working independently, you are encouraged to take a disciplined approach, select a weekly topic and to journal on at least three distinct days.

When you complete a topic, you are encouraged to synthesize your thoughts and to consider how you will apply new insights to your leadership.

Enjoy the journey!

SECTION 5

Connected Leadership Journaling Themes

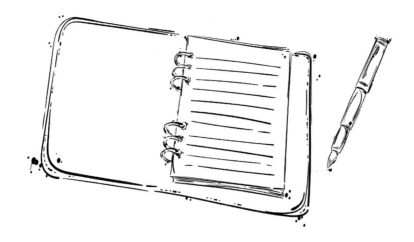

THEME ONE
The Leadership Connection

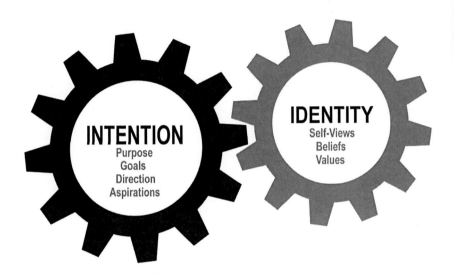

A little reflection will show us that every belief, even the simplest and most fundamental, goes beyond experience when regarded as a guide to our actions.

-William Kingdon Clifford, FRS

TOPIC 1

Examining Other Leaders

"Reflection is looking in so you can look out with a broader, bigger, and more accurate perspective."
-Mick Ukleja & Robert Lorber, Ph.D.

This topic's questions are designed for you to reflect on the type of leader traits that you admire and to examine the beliefs that you hold about the role and responsibilities of leadership.

Question 1:
Who are some leaders (contemporary or historical) that you admire? What do (or did) they say or do that garnered your admiration?

_____

_____

_____

_____

_____

_____

_____

_____

_____

_____

_____

_____

_____

_____

_____

Question 2:

What makes someone a leader? Consider characteristics, traits, skills, abilities, and knowledge areas.   How do you know a leader when you see one?

_____

_____

_____

_____

_____

_____

_____

_____

_____

_____

_____

_____

_____

_____

_____

_____

_____

_____

_____

_____

_____

_____

_____

_____

_____

_____

Question 3:

Think about a leader for whom you lost respect. What did he or she do or say that led to the change in your perception? What did you learn from this leader's words and actions?

_____

_____

_____

_____

_____

_____

_____

_____

_____

_____

_____

_____

_____

_____

_____

_____

_____

_____

_____

_____

_____

_____

_____

_____

_____

_____

_____

_____

TOPIC 2

Examining My Leadership

"The way we think about ourselves as leaders and what we believe leadership to be are important guides of subsequent thoughts and actions in the leadership domain."

-Nathan J. Hiller, Ph.D.

This topic's questions examine the beliefs that you hold about your own leadership—how you see yourself as a leader—along with defining moments that have impacted your leadership development. How you perceive yourself as a leader is a powerful predictor of how you will act as a leader.

Question 1:
When did you acknowledge to yourself or others that you are or could be a leader? Define in as much detail as possible the moment or moments that led to your belief that you could fulfill the role of leadership.

_____

_____

_____

_____

_____

_____

_____

_____

_____

_____

_____

_____

_____

Question 2:

If asked to give an "elevator speech" (a 30 second description) to someone regarding who you are as a leader, what would you say?

_____

_____

_____

_____

_____

_____

_____

_____

_____

_____

_____

_____

_____

_____

_____

_____

_____

_____

_____

_____

_____

_____

Question 3:

Describe some of the guiding principles of your leadership philosophy. In other words, what values, behaviors, practices, and considerations do you actively seek to incorporate into your work as a leader and would like others to see demonstrated in your example?

_____

_____

_____

_____

_____

_____

_____

_____

_____

_____

_____

_____

_____

_____

_____

_____

_____

_____

_____

_____

_____

_____

_____

_____

_____

TOPIC 3
My Leadership Experiences

"Leaders grow, they are not made."
-Peter F. Drucker, Ph.D.

You are molded by your experiences. Every good and bad leadership decision has informed your approach to leadership. In this topic, you are asked to consider early leadership experiences that you had, both good and bad, and their impact on your self-views as a leader.

Question 1:
Think about the first time you were placed in a formal position of leading others. Recall the thoughts and emotions that you felt around the experience. What about the experience made it clear to you that you were, or could be, a leader?

_____

_____

_____

_____

_____

_____

_____

_____

_____

_____

_____

_____

_____

_____

_____

Question 2:

Think about a time when you made a mistake while leading others early in your leadership experience. What happened and how did you handle it? What would you do differently now if you had it to do over again?

_____

_____

_____

_____

_____

_____

_____

_____

_____

_____

_____

_____

_____

_____

_____

_____

_____

_____

_____

_____

_____

_____

Question 3:

Think about a time you felt successful as a leader. What was the experience? What specifically did you do or say that helped create that success?

_____

_____

_____

_____

_____

_____

_____

_____

_____

_____

_____

_____

_____

_____

_____

_____

_____

_____

_____

_____

_____

_____

_____

_____

TOPIC 4
My Leadership Lessons

"Never regret the past. Accept it as the teacher it is."
-Robin Sharma

Through the course of your career, you have had experiences and opportunities that have further defined who you are as a leader. Reflect on the experiences, teachers, and the lessons learned over the course of your leadership journey.

Question 1:
Consider how your leadership has changed over time. What or who prompted those changes? What important watershed events significantly changed how you approach the role of a leader?

_____

_____

_____

_____

_____

_____

_____

_____

_____

_____

_____

_____

_____

_____

_____

Question 2:

If you could identify the most critical lesson learned in your leadership career, what would it be and why?

_____

_____

_____

_____

_____

_____

_____

_____

_____

_____

_____

_____

_____

_____

_____

_____

_____

_____

_____

_____

_____

_____

_____

_____

Question 3:
Consider a decision or action you took as a leader that you now believe was a mistake. What did you learn? How has your leadership changed because of that lesson?

_____

_____

_____

_____

_____

_____

_____

_____

_____

_____

_____

_____

_____

_____

_____

_____

_____

_____

_____

_____

_____

_____

_____

Synthesizing and Applying Theme:
Consider your entries for this theme. What insights did you gain? Is there anything you will seek to do more of, differently, or less of because of your reflection on the topics in this theme?

_____

_____

_____

_____

_____

_____

_____

_____

_____

_____

_____

_____

_____

_____

_____

_____

_____

_____

_____

_____

_____

_____

_____

_____

_____

THEME TWO
My Leader Intention

Our intention creates our reality.

-Wayne Dyer

TOPIC 1

My Leader Intention

"When you choose to benefit others before yourself, you are choosing to impact the trajectory of others. When you choose to empower others, you are choosing to increase your own influence and ultimately make your leadership come alive. When you choose to lead others with the right intent, you are giving others a great example of proper leadership."

-Jeremie Kubicek

Leaders have intent – a reason for acting. It can be negative or positive. It can be selfish or selfless. In this topic, you will begin to examine your intentions and your driving passion regarding your leadership.

Question 1:
What are your driving leadership intentions? Why do you lead? What do you want to accomplish in your role as a leader?

I LEAD THE SQL AREA BECAUSE I HAVE EXPERTISE I WANT TO SHARE W/ OTHERS AS OTHER SHARED W/ ME

I WANT TO CREATE A CENTER OF EXCELLENCE FOR PARTNERS + COLLEAGUES AT THE DATA SERVICES CAMER.

Question 2:

What are you most passionate about regarding your current leadership role? What is it about this role, activity, or relationship that accomplishes that which you intend? If you are an aspiring leader, what excites you the most about being a leader?

I AM PASSIONATE ABOUT THE ABILITY TO MAKE A DIFFERENCE FOR PARTNERS + COLLEAGUES.

COLLEAGUES LOOK FOR TRUSTED GUIDANCE

PARTNERS LOOK FOR RESOLUTIONS THAT HELP THEM TO RUN THEIR BUSINESS

AND I WANT THE TEAM TO BE EXCITED ABOUT BEING ABLE TO HAVE SUCH A POSITIVE IMPACT

Question 3:

What can others observe in your words and behavior that demonstrates what you believe to be your intention as a leader?

I WORK w/ AN OBVIOUS PASSION.

SOMETIMES I AM TOO DRIVEN SO I NEED TO LEARN TO SLOW DOWN + GET OTHERS ENGAGED TO COME ALONG FOR THE RIDE

TOPIC 2
The Influence of Intention

"...people who have purpose are motivated to pursue the most difficult problems."

-Janet Choi

Intention is the leadership accelerant. It provides a deliberate emphasis on moving in a certain direction, or for a certain purpose. If your intention changes so too, do your behaviors. In this topic, you will consider how your intention influences your thinking and behavior.

Question 1:
Consider an experience when your driving purpose helped you get through a difficult challenge. How did knowing your purpose help you deal with the difficulties you faced.

WHEN I LEFT VERIZON "THE NEST"
I WAS CHALLENGED W/ A GREATER
EXPECTATION TO PERFORM. ALTHOUGH
I WAS NEW TO THE COMPANY AND
I WAS YOUNGER THAN MANY, I
WAS ASKED TO DRIVE THE
DIRECTION OF THE DATABASE
WORLD.

THE DRIVE TO SUCCEED WAS
ABLE TO OVERCOME MY OWN
NERVOUSNESS OF THE
SITUATION

Question 2:

Consider a time when you were faced with a difficult decision. Who did you have to influence or be influenced by in order to make this decision. How did your intentions play into this decision?

OPEN CALLS WARE MADE FOR NEW STREAMS OF REVENUE BY THE CEO.

OUR AREA WAS ALWAYS CONSIDERED A "COST" AREA AND WAS FACED WITH HOW TO INFLUENCE THE CEO THAT:

1. WE WERE SERVICING PARTNERS
2. NOT MOVING THE COMPANY IN AN AREA WE DID NOT WANT TO BE
3. IT WOULD SUCCEED

Question 3:
Reflect on a difficult conversation - A time when you had to deliver bad news, redirect a poor performer, share a change in a long-standing expectation, confront a colleague, or other reasons that created stress or conflict. Reflect on your intentions behind these conversations. How did your intentions "show up" in the influence you sought and the way you engaged in the conversation?

DIRECT REPORT WAS STRUGGLING TO PERFORM AND WAS NOT SEEING THEMSELVES AS A FIT.

I WAS ABLE TO STEP THEIR FEARS BY MAKING THEM COMFORTABLE THAT "THERE WAS NO WRONG ANSWER"

ABLE TO CLEAR THEIR MIND, THEY BEGAN TO PERFORM.

TOPIC 3

Reconnecting with Intention

"When what you value and dream about doesn't match the life you are living, you have pain."

-Shannon L. Adler

Sometimes we feel disconnected from our work, our team, or our organization. In this topic, you will consider what you have done, or can do, when you find that your driving purpose does not align with your circumstances.

Question 1:
Reflect on a period when you felt you did not belong, a time when something restricted your ability to lead as you intended to lead or to be connected or aligned with others and the work at hand. How did you respond during that time? If you found yourself in a similar situation today what would you do differently?

- TIMES OF EVER CHANGING PRIORITIES

- TEAM IN TURMOIL

- DIDN'T EMBRACE THE CHANGE, GET BEHIND IT OR TRY TO UNDERSTAND IT

- COMPLETE OPPS ITE

Question 2:

Consider a time when you reacted to something or someone in the workplace that was not aligned with your intentions. What were the specific behaviors displayed? What did you do after you reacted? What would you do differently today?

A SHIFT TO MICROSERVICES (A TERM MISUSED) DID NOT SETTLE WELL. ALTHOUGH I DID NOT FIGHT IT, MY QUESTIONS GAVE THE OPPOSITE IMPRESSION

I TOED THE LINE

I WOULD HAVE STATED / WORDED MY QUESTIONS IN A WAY THAT CONVEYED BUY-IN BUT IN NEED OF CLARITY

Question 3:
Think about a time when you considered leaving, or actually chose to leave, a position or an organization. What about the position or organization contributed to your desire to separate yourself? What about your own wiring, expectations, or needs contributed to this state? What can these reflections teach you about what you need to find in your next position or organization?

I HAD REACHED A POINT WHERE GROWTH WAS BECOMING LIMITED.

THAT HAD BEEN A MAJOR TRADE OFF FOR COMPENSATION

I ALWAYS NEED THE ABILITY TO GROW

TOPIC 4
Sharing My Intention

"And it's those who start with why, that have the ability to inspire those around them..."

-Simon Sinek

Effective leaders understand what they want to accomplish and are driven to achieve their leadership purpose. They think that they can and will bring their very best to something they want to accomplish. The better able they are to articulate this intention, the more it serves to accelerate their work and the work of those they seek to inspire.

Question 1:
List those things you believe to be true about why you have accepted a leadership role. Try to summarize these beliefs into no more than three simple sentences.

I HAVE KNOWLEDGE TO SHARE.

I CAN MAKE A DIFFERENCE FOR OUR PARTNERS

I HAVE A PASSION FOR MY CRAFT

Question 2:

Reflect on a time when you believe you were the very best leader for the time and place. In other words, where all pistons were firing and you felt fully equipped to be leading others. If new to leadership, think about a time when you felt you were influential in a team setting. What was it about this situation that contributes to your positive appraisals?

LARGE LMS PROJECT AT VERIZON. I WAS DRIVING THE DATABASE SIDE OF THE PROJECT TECHNICALLY AND THE CODE SIDE FROM A PM PERSPECTIVE.

RUNNING ON ALL CYLINDERS IN EVERY WAY

Question 3:

Consider a time when you had a new person on your team, be it a team for which you were a member or a leader. What did you want the new team member to know about you, your beliefs, and your intentions? How did you share that information? How might you do a better job of communicating your beliefs and intentions the next time a new person joins your team?

WANT THEM TO KNOW MY PASSION FOR HELPING OTHERS

SHARED WHAT WE DID AND WERE RESPONSIBLE FOR

EXPLAIN MORE ON WHY WE DO THINGS WE DO

Synthesizing and Applying Theme:
Consider your entries for this theme. What insights did you gain?
Is there anything you will seek to do more of, differently, or less of
because of your reflection on the topics in this theme?

_____

_____

_____

_____

_____

_____

_____

_____

_____

_____

_____

_____

_____

_____

_____

_____

_____

_____

_____

_____

_____

_____

_____

_____

THEME THREE
My Leader Identity

IDENTITY
Self-Views
Beliefs
Values

Effective leaders in the 21ˢᵗ century must operate with a strong sense of their own identity, because along with it comes purpose and integrity, willingness to take risks, the ability to understand the importance of change and to be ready for it.

-Stedman Graham

TOPIC 1
My Leader Self-Construct

"The way we perceive ourselves, our self-concept or identity, has profound effects on the way we feel, think, and behave, and for the things we aim to achieve."
-Mark R. Learey, Ph.D. & June Price Tangney, Ph.D.

Self-construct is essentially synonymous with self-concept in that it represents the beliefs that we hold about ourselves in personal, relational, and collective terms. It is also a dynamic and ever-changing construct. For this topic, you will consider how, or even if, you define yourself as a leader.

Question 1:
Think about the last time you met a new group of people. When asked "what do you do?" how did you answer? What roles did you ascribe to yourself? Why did you select those roles?

DATABASE ARCHITECT +
ADMINISTRATOR

- DAY TO DAY IS VERY
TASK DRIVEN +
THE ABOVE BEST DESCRIBES
QUICKLY

- A BREAKOUT USUALLY FOLLOWS
BASED FURTHER EXPLAINING
WHAT THAT ENTAILS

Question 2:

Reflect on the roles you ascribe to yourself today. How does your assumption of those roles impact how you act? How might you act differently if you described yourself differently? (i.e. "I am leader in my organization." "I am the operations leader for my organization." "I am an IT professional.")

Although I lead the team, I usually blend in with my cohort as we collectively move tasks forward. I do this so as to make all feel they have equal say in our direction. My part as lead lies more in how I buffer the team from distraction.

Question 3:

Reflect on the last time you were hired or promoted to a new job. In what ways, if any, did the assumption of a new role change how you came to define yourself?

I AM NOT SURE IT CHANGED HOW I DEFINED MYSELF BY A LARGE DEGREE ASIDE FROM THE FACT THAT I WAS BECOMING MORE OF A "GO-TO" PERSON FOR ANSWERS WHEN TECHNICAL CHALLENGES ARE FACED.

TOPIC 2
My Leader Self-Esteem

"Everything that happens to you is a reflection of what you believe about yourself. We cannot outperform our level of self-esteem. We cannot draw to ourselves more than we think we are worth."

-Iyanla Vanzant

Self-esteem provides an affective component to the self-concept. It includes both positive and negative evaluations that a person holds about him or herself. It is the emotional component to the self-view. Think this topic about how you have measured and evaluated your own leadership.

Question 1:
If you were asked to rate your overall leadership effectiveness, what score would you give yourself? What are the positive and negative terms you would use to describe your leadership value?

6/10

POSITIVE
- LEAD BY EXAMPLE TECHNICALLY
- ORGANIZED
- DRIVEN

NEGATIVES
- PATIENCE
- TOLERANCE FOR LESS THAN
  FULL EFFORT

Question 2:
Think about a project or task that went well. How did you evaluate your contribution? Conversely, think of a project or task that did not go well. How did you evaluate your contribution?

EV RECOVERY
- WELL PREPARED
- WELL TEMPERED
- COMMUNICATED WELL

PATCH ADMIN PUSHES
- I WAS ABLE TO
  PREDICT ISSUES
- I WARNED OF ISSUES
- I COULD HAVE TRIED
  HARDER TO PREVENT
  THE ISSUES (EVEN THOUGH
  NOT MY RESPONSIBILITY)
  WHEN OTHER "LEADERS"
  DID NOT

- EFFECTIVELY MITIGATED
  ISSUES UPON OCCURRENCE

Question 3:

Consider a time when your self-esteem was negative (i.e. "I am a poor leader," "I am an ineffective leader."). How did such self-talk impact your future leadership behavior? Consider a time when your self-esteem was positive (i.e. "I am a good leader." "I am an effective leader."). How did such self-talk impact your future leadership behavior?

INABILITY TO GET NEW HIRES TO STICK

- ALTHOUGH THERE WERE PROPER REASONS FOR DISMISSAL, I ALWAYS TEND TO THINK THERE HAD TO BE SOMETHING I COULD HAVE DONE DIFFERENT TO CHANGE THE OUTCOME

- ALTERS HOW I APPROACH ALL ASPECTS OF THE ONBOARDING PROCESS

USUALLY MORE AROUND TECHNIQUE LEADERSHIP ON HOW TO EFFECTIVELY APPROACH A PROBLEM

- REINFORCES THAT MY THOUGHT PROCESS IS EFFECTIVE AND ADDS TO CONFIDENCE IN FUTURE PROJECTS

TOPIC 3

My Leader Self-Consistency

"If I say I'm going to do something, I do it. If I say I am going to be somewhere, I'm there. If I initiate a new business process or initiative, I follow through. In my experience, consistency is a must as you build and grow your business."

-Eric V. Holtzclaw

Self-consistency is a sense of continuity that is present in an individual's perceptions of him or herself. It includes the stability of past, present and future beliefs, and values that a person holds. Further it is the degree to which a person's values, beliefs, and temperament are stable and aligned with their behavior over time, across environments and with a variety of audiences. Consider how consistency can be demonstrated.

Question 1:
Think about a leader you know whose beliefs, or at least the intensity of his or her beliefs, changed when the audience changed. How does this inconsistency affect your willingness and your ability to follow this leader?

_____

_____

_____

_____

_____

_____

_____

_____

_____

_____

Question 2:

Consider beliefs and values that you carry with you from situation to situation - beliefs and values that are fully integrated into who you are. How do these beliefs and values impact choices you make about where to work, who to work with, and how you approach your work?

Question 3:

When exploration leads you to something that challenges a core belief or value, how do you address this disconnect? If the exploration leads you to change a core belief or value, how do you talk about this with your followers, peers, and others?

_____

_____

_____

_____

_____

_____

_____

_____

_____

_____

_____

_____

_____

_____

_____

_____

_____

_____

_____

_____

_____

_____

_____

TOPIC 4

My Leader Self-Efficacy

*"If you think you can do a thing or
think you can't do a thing, you're right."*

-Henry Ford

Self-efficacy refers to the beliefs that an individual has about his or her ability to act in ways necessary to successfully accomplish a goal. It is the level of confidence that a person holds in being able to successfully complete a task or a role. Reflect on how confidence has affected your leadership.

Question 1:
Think about aspects of your leadership that you do not think are "up to speed." Those areas where you believe you are inadequate or that significantly challenge your ability to perform as required. What are you doing (or should plan to do) to address those limitations?

_____

_____

_____

_____

_____

_____

_____

_____

_____

_____

_____

_____

Question 2:
Think about a project or task you led that went well. What aspects of your leadership were essential for that success? Think about a project or task you led that did not go well. What aspects of your leadership could have been enhanced to achieve a better result?

_____

_____

_____

_____

_____

_____

_____

_____

_____

_____

_____

_____

_____

_____

_____

_____

_____

_____

_____

_____

_____

_____

Question 3:

Reflect on your response to new and difficult leadership challenges. How do you feel and what do you do to address those difficulties? Does your response indicate you have a strong belief in your ability to lead others or do you find yourself looking to others to provide answers, solutions, or leadership?

_____

_____

_____

_____

_____

_____

_____

_____

_____

_____

_____

_____

_____

_____

_____

_____

_____

_____

_____

_____

_____

_____

_____

Synthesizing and Applying Theme:

Consider your entries for this theme. What insights did you gain? Is there anything you will seek to do more of, differently or less of because of your reflection on the topics in this theme?

_____

_____

_____

_____

_____

_____

_____

_____

_____

_____

_____

_____

_____

_____

_____

_____

_____

_____

_____

_____

_____

_____

_____

_____

_____

THEME FOUR
Examination

EXAMINATION
Looking Within
Considering Others
Considering Context

"Self-reflection allows you to gain clarity on issues, both personal and professional, because you have taken the time to think more deeply about them. The more self-reflective you are the easier it is to make choices that are in line with your values, with awareness of the full impact of your decisions.

Harry M. Jansen Kraemer, Jr

TOPIC 1
Self-Awareness

He who knows others is wise. He who knows himself is enlightened
-Lao Tzu

Like the emperor in the classic Hans Christian Anderson's, *The Emperor's New Clothes*, the unaware leader is blind to that which may negatively influence his relationship and effectiveness and to those strengths that he could use to maximize his leadership. In this topic, you will consider what you are doing and what more you can do to ensure you to ensure you know yourself.

Question 1:
What are you doing to routinely and rigorously self-evaluate your beliefs, behaviors, and pre-conceived notions? (i.e. assessments, 360° feedback.) What are you doing or can you do to be assured that your behavior is aligned with your stated beliefs?

360° REVIEWS

SET BETTER EXPECTATIONS
BETWEEN ME + MY
REPORTS AS TO WHAT
THEY WANT FROM ME

Question 2:

Think about a time when someone offered either unsolicited or solicited feedback on your leadership behavior or effectiveness. How did you respond at that time, and how did you address the suggestions that were offered to you? Consider how you might actively invite trusted and respected people in your circle to provide you with ideas on what you might do more of, differently, or less of that would help you be a better leader?

MY BOSS FELT I WAS NOT OPEN TO NEW PLATFORMS AS I EXPRESSED CONCERNS IN A WAY THAT CAME OFF AS PUSHBACK

- I ALTERED MY WAY OF PRESENTING MY QUESTIONS

Question 3:

Consider a time when you were challenged to listen before speaking. What was the outcome of this challenge? Did you manage to listen and hold your own response? If so, what did you learn that you might not otherwise have learned had you spoken first? If you did not focus on listening, what opportunities to learn from others have you missed by failing to listen first?

YES - ALWAYS A CHALLENGE AS
I WANT TO GET TO
THE CHASE

DID NOT NECESARRILY LEARN
BUT MY PART WAS
RECEIVED BETTER

TOPIC 2
Exploring Other's Perspectives

"If we only discuss issues with people who agree with us we stop learning.

-Jesse Lyn Stoner, Ed.D.

The most influential leader is one who actively seeks differing perceptions and opinions and displays behaviors that invite the alternative viewpoint. For this topic, you will evaluate yourself on these practices and determine ways you can expand your capacity to learn from the ideas and perspectives of others.

Question 1:
Think about a recent disagreement you have had with someone that was borne from conflicting positions. What did you really want? What did the other person really want? What would have been different if both of you focused on your real interests behind your positions?

WE WANTED THE SAME THING
AS IT TURNED OUT BUT
APPROACHED FROM DIFFERENT
ANGLES / PERSPECTIVES.

IF WE HAD DEFINED THINGS
BETTER UP FRONT WE COULD
HAVE AVOIDED THE ISSUE
+ SAVED TIME

Question 2:
Think about a time when you had a vastly different perception of a situation from someone else. What do you think caused this disconnect? What would you do differently if you had an opportunity to better understand the basis of their perspective?

_____

_____

_____

_____

_____

_____

_____

_____

_____

_____

_____

_____

_____

_____

_____

_____

_____

_____

_____

_____

_____

Question 3:
Consider the messages and the methods you employ (or should employ) to solicit perceptions that are different from your own. Consider how you give permission, encouragement, safety, and value to someone who may hold a contrary viewpoint. Consider what you may do, either intentionally or unintentionally, to discourage others from sharing their viewpoints.

TOPIC 3

Contextual Awareness

"It over simplifies the situation in large organizations to assume there is only one culture... and it's risky for new leaders to ignore the sub-cultures."

-Rolfe Winkler

We have observed and read about numerous leaders who were hired because of their enormous success in one organization only to be quickly fired because they failed to meet expectations. Leaders do not suddenly forget how to lead, but they can forget to consider the context in which they are leading. In this topic, you will reflect on the value of understanding the context (i.e., culture, forces, situational parameters) in which you are now leading or considering leading.

Question 1:
Reflect on a time when you found yourself unhappy in a job or organization. What things did you learn in the early months of your tenure that you wish you had known before accepting the job? What did you learn to do before accepting your next job to avoid these kinds of surprises?

_____

_____

_____

_____

_____

_____

_____

_____

_____

Question 2:

Consider your own beliefs about collaboration and teamwork?
Next consider how your organization's structure positively or
negatively impacts collaboration and teamwork. How might this
knowledge impact how you lead?

Question 3:

Consider how your own leadership behavior has historically prioritized the needs and expectations of employees, customers, and other stakeholders. Compare this to the priority your organization places (or fails to place) on employees, customers, or other stakeholders. How will this insight influence your leadership choices and behaviors, or even your choice to remain with the organization?

_____

_____

_____

_____

_____

_____

_____

_____

_____

_____

_____

_____

_____

_____

_____

_____

_____

_____

_____

_____

TOPIC 4
Leadership and Values

"Transcendent values like trust and integrity literally translate into revenue, profits and prosperity."

-Patricia Aburdene

Values are an important currency in institutions. Today's business leaders are expected to reflect personal values in their daily behaviors and to clarify and build collective values in their teams and organizations. For this topic, you will explore your values, your organization's values, and how they help to ground your leadership approach.

Question 1:
What do you do to promote both organizational and personal values in your area of responsibility? How do you acknowledge the protection or promotion of values by your employees or co-workers? What other methods can you consider adopting or adapting to more clearly and more consistently support and reinforce the demonstration of values-centered behaviors?

_____

_____

_____

_____

_____

_____

_____

_____

_____

_____

_____

_____

Question 2:

Think about employee, supervisor, or co-worker behaviors and attitudes that you consider deal breakers with regard to your personal values. Why do these particular behaviors elicit such a strong response? How have these prior experiences strengthened why you view these behaviors as deal breakers?

_____

_____

_____

_____

_____

_____

_____

_____

_____

_____

_____

_____

_____

_____

_____

_____

_____

_____

_____

_____

_____

_____

Question 3:

Think about a time when the behaviors that you observed in employees or co-workers were inconsistent with your values and yet you chose not to intervene or speak up. In a values-centered workplace, is there room to have two categories of values violations - those situations where we will intervene readily and those where we won't at all? Where is your line in the sand?

_____

_____

_____

_____

_____

_____

_____

_____

_____

_____

_____

_____

_____

_____

_____

_____

_____

_____

_____

_____

_____

_____

_____

_____

_____

Synthesizing and Applying Theme:
Consider your entries for this theme. What insights did you gain?
Is there anything you will seek to do more of, differently, or less of
because of your reflection on the topics in this theme?

_____

_____

_____

_____

_____

_____

_____

_____

_____

_____

_____

_____

_____

_____

_____

_____

_____

_____

_____

_____

_____

_____

_____

_____

THEME FIVE

Exploration

We shall not cease from exploration, and the end of all our exploring will be to arrive where we started and know the place for the first time.

-T. S. Eliot

TOPIC 1
Looking Beyond Yourself

"It is the mark of an educated mind to be able to entertain a thought without accepting it."

-Aristotle

With this topic, you will be asked to reflect upon activities and behaviors that facilitate an exploration mindset and a thinking culture. Consider those behaviors you reinforce that facilitate effective thinking along with methods for ensuring that you and others are actively exploring, outside of your normal channels as you gather information and evaluate options including those challenge the status quo and seek out best and next practices.

Question 1:
Think about a time when you were in a problem solving or brainstorming session with staff that generated and examined a number of potentially effective options. What did the facilitator do that helped to create this environment?

_____

_____

_____

_____

_____

_____

_____

_____

_____

_____

_____

Question 2:

Think about a time when an individual brought you an "out of the box" idea or solution for a problem you were facing. How did you respond? Was your response one that rewarded this kind of thinking or punished it?

_____

_____

_____

_____

_____

_____

_____

_____

_____

_____

_____

_____

_____

_____

_____

_____

_____

_____

_____

_____

_____

_____

Question 3:

What do you do to encourage others to stretch and challenge the limits of their thinking? What do you need to do to ensure that their thinking continues to be expanded and refined? (i.e. exploration of analogous field solutions, consideration of the contrary opinion, learning from lessons of history).

_____

_____

_____

_____

_____

_____

_____

_____

_____

_____

_____

_____

_____

_____

_____

_____

_____

_____

_____

_____

_____

_____

TOPIC 2

Being Open to Influence

"It would be difficult to exaggerate the degree to which we are influenced by those we influence."

-Eric Hoffer

Influence is reciprocal. People are more willing to listen and consider your ideas if they believe you are willing to give their ideas respectful consideration. For this topic, you will explore ways to ensure that you are actively seeking and responding to the influence of others.

Question 1:
Think about a time when you changed your position on an important issue as a result of another person's influence. What did they do to influence you to change your position? What other elements were involved in the reversal?

_____

_____

_____

_____

_____

_____

_____

_____

_____

_____

_____

_____

_____

Question 2:

Consider a time when someone tried to influence you and you resisted. What increased your resistance? Did you resist information or an approach that could have been superior to your own or were you right in standing firm? What could have lessened or eliminated your resistance?

Question 3:

To be influenced we must listen, consider, and evaluate what is said. Consider an effort to persuade you to act or even think differently to which you reacted negatively. What might you have done to discard, discredit, or simply ignore what was being asked of you before fully hearing, considering, or evaluating the message?

_____

_____

_____

_____

_____

_____

_____

_____

_____

_____

_____

_____

_____

_____

_____

_____

_____

_____

_____

_____

_____

_____

_____

_____

TOPIC 3
Fostering Creativity & Innovation

"Creativity is thinking up new things.
Innovation is doing new things.
-Theodore Levitt, Ph.D.

Creativity and innovation are increasingly considered mandatory elements of today's organizations. With today's increasingly competitive and crowded marketplaces, the leader who can explore and facilitate new and different thinking can achieve or retain a competitive edge. This topic you will reflect upon behaviors that are critical for fostering a creative and innovative culture.

Question 1:
Consider a time when you took on a creative task or assignment that was out of your comfort zone and required "out of the box" thinking. What motivated you to do this? What were the results? How did you, or others, help to facilitate the identification of creative solutions?

_____

_____

_____

_____

_____

_____

_____

_____

_____

Question 2:

Consider messages that you give your staff regarding risk-taking and innovation. What do you say or do that conveys where the "above the waterline" decisions are? How do you react to others when mistakes are made as part of the creative process?

_____

_____

_____

_____

_____

_____

_____

_____

_____

_____

_____

_____

_____

_____

_____

_____

_____

_____

_____

_____

_____

_____

_____

Question 3:
Think about a time when you were working on a team that you believed was particularly creative and innovative. What behaviors and interactions were in place that created this environment? What did the leader do to facilitate this type of collaborative innovative thinking? How can this be duplicated?

_____

_____

_____

_____

_____

_____

_____

_____

_____

_____

_____

_____

_____

_____

_____

_____

_____

_____

_____

_____

_____

_____

_____

TOPIC 4

Exploring with Creative Thinking

*"Once we rid ourselves of traditional thinking,
we can get on with creating the future.*

-James Bertrand

Many people see creativity as lightening in a bottle — hard to capture or recreate. Effective leaders, however, understand the link between the work environment, rewards, and motivations on the creative capacity of their teams. This topic you will reflect upon ways to further explore and tap the creative capacity of your team and organization to find new opportunities.

Question 1:
Where do the untapped opportunities lie for your organization? For your team? What can you do to harvest those opportunities?

_____

_____

_____

_____

_____

_____

_____

_____

_____

_____

_____

_____

Question 2:

What behaviors do you consistently exhibit to foster exploration, curiosity, and inquiry among your team? How do you facilitate discussions around new opportunities? What do you need to do differently to expand the ability to identify and capitalize on opportunities among your team?

Question 3:

Consider how you currently facilitate creative problem solving. What could be employed to allow for more unbounded creativity in thoughts and ideas?

_____

_____

_____

_____

_____

_____

_____

_____

_____

_____

_____

_____

_____

_____

_____

_____

_____

_____

_____

_____

_____

_____

_____

_____

Synthesizing and Applying Theme:
Consider your entries for this theme. What insights did you gain?
Is there anything you will seek to do more of, differently, or less of
because of your reflection on the topics in this theme?

_____

_____

_____

_____

_____

_____

_____

_____

_____

_____

_____

_____

_____

_____

_____

_____

_____

_____

_____

_____

_____

_____

THEME SIX
Enlistment

The key to successful leadership today is influence, *not* *authority.*

-Kenneth Blanchard, Ph.D.

TOPIC 1

Casting a Compelling Vision

"The very essence of leadership is that you have a vision. It's got to be a vision you articulate clearly and forcefully on every occasion. You cannot blow an uncertain trumpet."

-Rev. Theodore Hesburgh

Leaders imagine new realities. They look for things that are broken and show others how to fix them. They look for things that are working and show others how to make them better. They look for opportunities that changes will bring and show others how to leverage those changes for greater results. Leaders point to a destination and get others to follow with a compelling vision of what the future could look like. Reflect on your experiences with casting and following a vision.

Question 1:
Consider the process that you feel most comfortable with when you are planning to establish a new direction for your team. What are some of the essential elements of your approach? How effective has your approach been in the past?

_____

_____

_____

_____

_____

_____

_____

_____

_____

_____

Question 2:

Think about a time when a leader moved you to go into a new direction. What did the leader do or say to clarify how the future would be different from or better than the past? What compelled you to follow?

- PAINT PERSPECTIVE / PICTURE
  - OUTCOMES ETC

- HEALTHY DEBATE

Question 3:

Creating a vision also means you need to consider what you should let go of or discontinue. What process do you use when writing a vision statement to determine what you should leave out or leave behind?

- USE GOOD + BAD EXAMPLES

- VERB IDENTIFICATION

TOPIC 2

Generating Buy-In

"If you believe lack of authority keeps you from leading effectively, it's time to rethink your understanding of leadership."
-Mike Bonem & Roger Patterson

A vision is just a daydream if the leader cannot get others to share that vision and to follow it in a purposeful way. A critical task of the leader is not only to cast a compelling vision, but also to engage others in its pursuit. Reflect on techniques and behaviors that help enlist others in your vision.

Question 1:
Think about a time that you had a great idea for a new direction and were unsuccessful in getting others to join you? What were the barriers? What would you do differently now with the benefit of hindsight?

_____

_____

_____

_____

_____

_____

_____

_____

_____

_____

_____

_____

_____

Question 2:

What are some of your "go to" methods for enlisting others to follow you in a certain direction? What do you do, in addition to clarifying the new path, that you believe compels others to want to follow you?

_____

_____

_____

_____

_____

_____

_____

_____

_____

_____

_____

_____

_____

_____

_____

_____

_____

_____

_____

_____

_____

_____

_____

_____

Question 3:
When you cannot get the followership that you expect, what are some of the things you do (or plan to do) in order to get people to follow?

_____

_____

_____

_____

_____

_____

_____

_____

_____

_____

_____

_____

_____

_____

_____

_____

_____

_____

_____

_____

_____

_____

_____

_____

_____

_____

_____

TOPIC 3
The Language of Influence

*"Words, like eyeglasses, blur everything that they
do not make clearer."*

-Joseph Joubert

We are more likely to be influenced when the new thinking or actions connect to our past successes, align with our values, or somehow supports our own aspirations. For this topic, reflect on times when your words, stories, or images resonated in ways that influenced others.

Question 1:
Consider the Gettysburg Address. In a few words Lincoln took the listener back to what he valued and then challenged the listener to take on the "unfinished business." Lincoln made a powerful connection between the listeners' collective past with the future he envisioned. How have you used, or could you use, this technique?

_____

_____

_____

_____

_____

_____

_____

_____

_____

_____

_____

_____

Question 2:

Another famous influential speech was Martin Luther King's "I Have a Dream." One of the reasons it was so effective was because of Dr. King's effective use of imagery to describe the dream broadly enough that each listener could see him or herself in that future, and narrow enough that each listener could determine what he or she needed to do to make the dream real. How have you used, or could you use, imagery to help a person you want to influence imagine him or herself in your new reality?

_____

_____

_____

_____

_____

_____

_____

_____

_____

_____

_____

_____

_____

_____

_____

_____

_____

_____

_____

_____

_____

Question 3:

Think about a time when you were influenced to act or think differently. What words or images were used to convince you? How did these words or images compel you to action?

_____

_____

_____

_____

_____

_____

_____

_____

_____

_____

_____

_____

_____

_____

_____

_____

_____

_____

_____

_____

_____

_____

_____

_____

_____

TOPIC 4
Enlisting through Influence

"The greatest ability in business is to get along with others and to influence their actions."

-John Hancock

Leaders hope to influence the thinking and actions of others. To be influential, you must understand and value the perspective of others, and be open to their influence while you attempt to influence them. In today's conceptual age where ascribed authority has little hold over employees, influence skills are even more critical. You must find effective ways of convincing people of the new way and to galvanize both commitment and action to ensure organizational success. This topic you will think of methods to increase your influence.

Question 1:
Think about a recent time when you were able to convince a group of people to change direction and to follow your recommendation. What did you say or do that got them to support you? How critical was your prior track record in getting others to follow? How would your experience have changed if you were new to the team?

_____

_____

_____

_____

_____

_____

_____

_____

_____

_____

Question 2:

What are some potential behaviors that you might demonstrate that could be working at cross purposes with getting others to agree with your ideas or approach? Challenge yourself to identify at least three things that you might do that could be derailing your success in enlisting others to follow your way of thinking.

_____

_____

_____

_____

_____

_____

_____

_____

_____

_____

_____

_____

_____

_____

_____

_____

_____

_____

_____

_____

_____

Question 3:

What does it take for someone to persuade you or "win you over" to his or her way of thinking? Are their different standards when others are attempting to convince you than when you are trying to convince others?

_____

_____

_____

_____

_____

_____

_____

_____

_____

_____

_____

_____

_____

_____

_____

_____

_____

_____

_____

_____

_____

_____

_____

_____

Synthesizing and Applying Theme:
Consider your entries for this theme. What insights did you gain? Is there anything you will seek to do more of, differently, or less of because of your reflection on the topics in this theme?

_____

_____

_____

_____

_____

_____

_____

_____

_____

_____

_____

_____

_____

_____

_____

_____

_____

_____

_____

_____

_____

_____

_____

Execution

Success doesn't necessarily come from breakthrough innovation but from flawless execution. A great strategy alone won't win a game or a battle; the win comes from basic blocking and tackling.

-Naveen Jain

TOPIC 1

Executing My Priorities

"Decide what you want, decide what you are willing to exchange for it, establish your priorities and go to work."

-H. L. Hunt

A leader cannot do everything. Research shows that the more priorities a leader has, the less he or she will successfully accomplish. Given that every leader must face personal capacity limits along with limited organizational time, resources, and money, what, then, become the most important priorities? Reflect on your process for keeping the focus on actions that move towards the vision.

Question 1:
Think of a time when something urgent took time, energy, and effort away those activities that had a direct impact on reaching the vision. How did you deal with the competing demand? Would you act the same way today?

_____

_____

_____

_____

_____

_____

_____

_____

_____

_____

_____

_____

Question 2:
Your priorities reveal what is most important to you. Identify your work and personal priorities and reflect on how they play out in how you spend your time and energy. Are there any places of misalignment? What do you need to do to bring your efforts back to those that drive toward the vision?

_____

_____

_____

_____

_____

_____

_____

_____

_____

_____

_____

_____

_____

_____

_____

_____

_____

_____

_____

_____

_____

_____

_____

Question 3:

Consider what others who work with and/or for you would say are your driving priorities. What do you think they would say and why? What in your behaviors conveys to others the level of your commitment to the vision?

_____

_____

_____

_____

_____

_____

_____

_____

_____

_____

_____

_____

_____

_____

_____

_____

_____

_____

_____

_____

_____

TOPIC 2
Cultivating Collaboration

"If you have an apple and I have an apple and we exchange these apples, then you and I will still each have one apple. But if you have an idea and I have an idea and we exchange these ideas, then each of us will have two ideas.

-George Bernard Shaw

When we learn to collaborate at the right time and in the right ways we achieve more than we can achieve alone or in our own silos. Leaders are charged with teaching others how to break down barriers and to build the systems and relationships that cultivate rather than restrict collaboration. This topic you will reflect on what you have learned about collaboration.

Question 1:
Consider the key people in your organization that you must currently work with on a regular basis to achieve results. Evaluate the level of collaboration you have with each of these people. What, if anything, do you need to adjust in any of these relationships?

_____

_____

_____

_____

_____

_____

_____

_____

_____

_____

_____

Question 2:

Consider people with whom you work with on a regular basis and with whom you have difficulty collaborating. What makes collaboration difficult with these people? What have you done in the past to build stronger relationships with these people? What remains to be done?

_____

_____

_____

_____

_____

_____

_____

_____

_____

_____

_____

_____

_____

_____

_____

_____

_____

_____

_____

_____

_____

_____

_____

Question 3:

Consider a time when you attempted to share an idea or implement a solution and were met with resistance. What were the factors that created the resistance? What could you have to knock down the barriers to more collaboration around the idea or solution?

_____

_____

_____

_____

_____

_____

_____

_____

_____

_____

_____

_____

_____

_____

_____

_____

_____

_____

_____

_____

_____

_____

TOPIC 3
Ethical Decision-Making

"Whoever is careless with the trust in small matters cannot be trusted with important matters."

-Albert Einstein, Ph.D.

Over recent years, organizations have been pulled into the ethical fray. Leaders have made decisions that forever changed their reputations and the reputations of their organizations. Focus on those values that drive your own decision-making, examine personal vulnerabilities, and consider behaviors to help insulate you from ethical breaches.

Question 1:
Consider your personal criteria for making business decisions. If you were to have an "elevator conversation" with a new team member, what would be your bulleted list of decision-making criteria? What priority have you placed on criteria related to ethics?

_____

_____

_____

_____

_____

_____

_____

_____

_____

_____

_____

_____

_____

Question 2:
Reflect on times when you have found yourself or others around you applying what can best be called "situational ethics." In what ways did you or others seek to rationalize behavior that you now believe did not reflect your highest standards? What were the short and long-term consequences of applying a situational standard? What would you do differently?

_____

_____

_____

_____

_____

_____

_____

_____

_____

_____

_____

_____

_____

_____

_____

_____

_____

_____

_____

_____

_____

_____

_____

Question 3:
Consider what others who work with you and for you would say about your decision-making. Is there anything they could say, or any example they could cite, that would reveal the degree to which ethics or values are reflected in your decisions? What do you think they would say and why? What do you need to do in response?

_____

_____

_____

_____

_____

_____

_____

_____

_____

_____

_____

_____

_____

_____

_____

_____

_____

_____

_____

_____

_____

_____

_____

_____

TOPIC 4
Staying the Course

"The secret of success is constancy of purpose."

-Benjamin Disraeli

For many leaders, creating the "new way" is where all the fun resides. For others, satisfaction comes in the day-to-day pursuit of the plan. Regardless of personal style and work preferences, you must become proficient in both creating and sustaining vision if you are going to provide the maximum benefit to your organization. Examine ways to keep the vision fresh and how to control that vision for periods when best efforts and plans get derailed.

Question 1:
When the vision becomes stale or less critical then when it was cast, what do you do in order to keep the vision fresh and current?

_____

_____

_____

_____

_____

_____

_____

_____

_____

_____

_____

_____

Question 2:

What have you done in the past when you were involved with a project that got off course? You might have been a leader, a follower, or a team member. Think about one thing you could have done that may have helped to correct the course.

_____

_____

_____

_____

_____

_____

_____

_____

_____

_____

_____

_____

_____

_____

_____

_____

_____

_____

_____

_____

_____

_____

Question 3:

How do you address the complacency of staff that often happens in the middle of project? How can you get them engaged or reengaged?

_____

_____

_____

_____

_____

_____

_____

_____

_____

_____

_____

_____

_____

_____

_____

_____

_____

_____

_____

_____

_____

_____

_____

_____

Synthesizing and Applying Theme:
Consider your entries for this theme. What insights did you gain?
Is there anything you will seek to do more of, differently, or less of
because of your reflection on the topics in this theme?

_____

_____

_____

_____

_____

_____

_____

_____

_____

_____

_____

_____

_____

_____

_____

_____

_____

_____

_____

_____

_____

_____

_____

_____

_____

_____

_____

_____

THEME EIGHT

Your Leader P.O.V.®

Leadership encompasses may things, and the "work" of a leader at any level in an organization demands a certain kind of self-awareness and focused attention.

- Ram Charan, Ph.D.

TOPIC 1

Your Leadership Capacity

"People with a high degree of personal mastery are acutely aware of their own ignorance, incompetency and growth areas. But they are also deeply self-confident."

-Peter Senge, Ph.D.

At the end of this theme you will be asked to create a 200 to 500-word Leader P.O.V.® statement. It should be written in a way that clearly yet concisely conveys the essence of your leadership to a reader or a listener.

A strong leadership self-identity is not only beneficial, but also critical to your success as a leader. Your journaling has helped you create, re-examine, update, and even strengthen your leadership self-identity. Your journaling also guided you as you worked to clearly articulate your Leader P.O.V.® in a concise, memorable, and compelling manner.

As you near the end of your exploration, it is time to reflect on the prior topics of journal entries in anticipating of writing and sharing a brief statement summarizing your leadership point of view. The journaling assignments have been designed to prompt your critical thinking and increase your awareness.

This topic you will focus on questions that will help inform your Leader P.O.V.® statement by focusing on your current leadership strengths, challenges, and developmental opportunities.

Question 1:

What is your "competitive advantage" as a leader? In other words, what strength differentiates you from others and positions you to produce at a superior level in comparison to others? What three things can you do to further develop this strength?

_____

_____

_____

_____

_____

_____

_____

_____

_____

_____

_____

_____

_____

_____

_____

_____

_____

_____

_____

_____

_____

_____

_____

_____

_____

Question 2:

Identify the one developmental area that you believe, once addressed, would help you to be even more effective in your current role (or in a role you aspire to obtain). How do you know that this is an area of development for you? What do you need to do to address this area in the short-term and long-term?

_____

_____

_____

_____

_____

_____

_____

_____

_____

_____

_____

_____

_____

_____

_____

_____

_____

_____

_____

_____

_____

_____

_____

_____

Question 3:

Identify three insights you have developed about yourself that are relevant to the way that you lead or work. How have you used these insights? What additional questions should you be asking yourself about your current leadership aptitude, awareness, and abilities?

_____

_____

_____

_____

_____

_____

_____

_____

_____

_____

_____

_____

_____

_____

_____

_____

_____

_____

_____

_____

_____

_____

_____

_____

TOPIC 2
What Is Your Leader P.O.V.®

"Without reflection, we go blindly on our way, creating unintended consequences, and failing to achieve anything useful."
-Margaret Wheatly, Ph.D.

Your Leader P.O.V.® statement is a highly personalized philosophy of leadership shaped by your prior experiences and changed, clarified, or strengthened by insights gained from journaling and new learning.

This topic you will focus on questions that will help inform your Leader P.O.V.® statement by focusing on that which your Leader P.O.V.® should tell others about you and your leadership.

Question 1:
Capture what you believe to be the role, responsibilities, and relationships of leaders and followers and how you personally define leadership.

_____

_____

_____

_____

_____

_____

_____

_____

_____

_____

_____

_____

Question 2:

Reflect back on your leadership intention about which you previously journaled. Consider subsequent journaling and learning as you share why you initially chose to be a leader, why you continue to choose to serve as a leader, and what you hope to accomplish as a leader.

_____

_____

_____

_____

_____

_____

_____

_____

_____

_____

_____

_____

_____

_____

_____

_____

_____

_____

_____

_____

_____

_____

_____

Question 3:

Review your prior journaling and learning as you articulate the expectations you have of yourself and others based on guiding principles and non-negotiables that influence you as a leader.

_____

_____

_____

_____

_____

_____

_____

_____

_____

_____

_____

_____

_____

_____

_____

_____

_____

_____

_____

_____

_____

_____

_____

_____

TOPIC 3

Continuous Reflection

Leadership and learning are indispensable to each other.
                                                        -John F. Kennedy

Leader P.O.V.® Statements may also include insights about how you plan to pursue leadership mastery and strengthen your leader effectiveness. This topic will help you determine what you might choose to share about your own learning with regard to leadership.

Question 1:
Consider what you do now and what you will do going forward to routinely examine the values, guiding principles, strengths, and weaknesses of yourself and others, and the context in which you find yourself leading? (Examination)

_____

_____

_____

_____

_____

_____

_____

_____

_____

_____

_____

_____

_____

_____

Question 2:

Consider how you actively explore and learn from: historical and contemporary leaders; the successes and failure of your own team and those outside of your team, your organization, your industry, or your profession; and the opinions and logic of those who agree and those who disagree with you. What approaches best equip you with new learning in order to effectively act? (Explore)

Question 3:

Based on what you have learned about your leadership, the people you lead, and the context in which you lead, what might you do to ensure that you stay focused on those actions you need to take as leader to enlist others. (Enlist)

_____

_____

_____

_____

_____

_____

_____

_____

_____

_____

_____

_____

_____

_____

_____

_____

_____

_____

_____

_____

_____

_____

_____

Question 4:
What steps will you take to ensure that you continue to increase your execution effectiveness – that you are able to guide the selection of the highest leverage priorities and foster accountability for results over effort? (Execute)

_____

_____

_____

_____

_____

_____

_____

_____

_____

_____

_____

_____

_____

_____

_____

_____

_____

_____

_____

_____

_____

_____

_____

_____

_____

TOPIC 4

Writing Your Leader P.O.V.®

Create your 200 to 500-word, compelling, memorable, and repeatable Leader P.O.V.® statement. It should be written in a way that clearly yet concisely conveys the essence of your leadership to a reader or a listener. It should reveal who you are as a leader by candidly and personally describing your leadership.

While writing and speaking style will influence your Leader P.O.V.® statement, you are encouraged to employ one or more of the following suggestions as they have been found to increase the memorability and repeatability of your statement.

- A repeated or parallel phrase that marks each new point makes it easier for the reader or listener to focus on and listen for the most important points. For example, "I believe that, as a leader, I…."

- Stories, metaphors, and analogies give the reader or listener a way to visualize what you are saying and therefore make it easier to remember. Personal stories, versus the stories of another, create a more genuine statement.

- "I" statements and other first-person references versus the use of "a leader" are more personal and demonstrate the message is integrated into your personal belief system.

- Limit your key points to five or less. Remember this is that which is most important to you.

_____

_____

_____

_____

_____

_____

SECTION SIX
Additional Journaling Themes

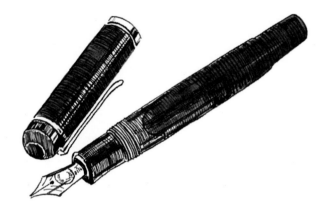

We have provided seven additional themes around which you may choose to journal. They include leadership competencies that have been found to be important for leadership success by organizations that have used the first edition of this journal. By reflecting on these additional journal themes, you can discover how you might better develop your abilities in these areas.

The themes are:

Leading Talent

Developing Others

Conflict

Change

Strategy

Sustaining Forward Momentum

Connected Communications

THEME NINE
Leading Talent

Leadership is lifting a person's vision to higher sights, the raising of a person's performance to a higher standard, the building of personality beyond its normal limitations.

-Peter F. Drucker, Ph.D.

TOPIC 1
Selecting Talent

"We expected that good-to-great leaders would begin by setting a new vision and strategy. We found instead that they first got the right people on the bus, the wrong people off the bus, and the right people in the right seat—and then figured out where to drive it."
-Jim Collins, Ph.D.

As Collins suggests, great leaders prioritize talent selection as a central strategic objective. If you do not have the right people, it really does not matter if you have the right strategy. This topic, you will reflect on your criteria for selecting team members.

Question 1:
When selecting a new team member, what skills, attributes, and talents are indispensable to you regardless of the specific job duties?

_____

_____

_____

_____

_____

_____

_____

_____

_____

_____

_____

_____

_____

Question 2:

Before a new member joins your team, what are the three most important things to convey to them regarding your team's culture, processes, and dynamic? How do you verify candidates are aligned and able to act accordingly?

_____

_____

_____

_____

_____

_____

_____

_____

_____

_____

_____

_____

_____

_____

_____

_____

_____

_____

_____

_____

_____

_____

Question 3:

For many leaders, whether consciously or unconsciously, selection decisions are biased toward candidates that look, think, and believe in ways similar to the person making the selection decision. Consider how this bias can both help and hurt an organization. What can be done to suspend this inclination to "hire or replicate the self?"

_____

_____

_____

_____

_____

_____

_____

_____

_____

_____

_____

_____

_____

_____

_____

_____

_____

_____

_____

_____

_____

_____

_____

TOPIC 2

Motivating and Rewarding

"The only happy people I know are the ones who are working well at something they consider important."

-Abraham Maslow, Ph.D.

Leaders are challenged to create environments that are motivating, define tasks that inspire best efforts, and reward people for doing the right things at the highest possible performance level. During this theme, you will reflect on what you have learned about motivating and rewarding others.

Question 1:
What does your experience tell you about the value of external rewards and how they are delivered?

_____

_____

_____

_____

_____

_____

_____

_____

_____

_____

_____

_____

_____

Question 2:

What does your experience tell you about the value of intrinsic and extrinsic motivation? How do you (or can you) best promote both sources of motivation in yourself and in others?

Question 3:

What have you done to help others link their current work to a sense of purpose? To something they believe is important?

_____

_____

_____

_____

_____

_____

_____

_____

_____

_____

_____

_____

_____

_____

_____

_____

_____

_____

_____

_____

_____

_____

_____

_____

TOPIC 3
Equipping Others

"Rather than dictating the actions that people must take, pull platforms provide people with the tools and resources (including connections to other people) required for them to take initiative and creatively address opportunities as they arise."
-John Hagel III, J.D., John Seely Brown, Ph.D. & Lang Davison

For this topic, you will consider how you equip your team to effectively execute—with consideration given to behaviors that lead to autonomy, effectiveness, creativity, and innovation.

Question 1:
What methods do you employ to determine the needs of your team? What systems do you put in place to ensure that they can get the resources that they need to do the most effective job?

_____

_____

_____

_____

_____

_____

_____

_____

_____

_____

_____

_____

_____

Question 2:

What is your leadership style as it relates to the level of autonomy and independence that you provide to your team or to individual team members?

_____

_____

_____

_____

_____

_____

_____

_____

_____

_____

_____

_____

_____

_____

_____

_____

_____

_____

_____

_____

_____

_____

_____

_____

_____

Question 3:

Think about your process for deciding when and how to help people get what they want versus helping them to get what they need. How do you proceed when what the person wants is ultimately not what they need?

_____

_____

_____

_____

_____

_____

_____

_____

_____

_____

_____

_____

_____

_____

_____

_____

_____

_____

_____

_____

_____

_____

_____

TOPIC 4

Retaining Talent

"...in-the-loop employees feel strong connections to the company. Connected employees jump into a major project, freely contribute their ideas and energy, and recommit themselves to company goals."
-Jim Harris, Ph.D., and Joan Brannick, Ph.D.

Retaining employees is, in large part, a reflection of how well you can engage them and keep them engaged. For this topic, you will examine your beliefs and practices regarding employee engagement and retention.

Question 1:
What do you believe are the most important practices and incentives for retaining your current team members? How do you know that these are THE factors?

_____

_____

_____

_____

_____

_____

_____

_____

_____

_____

_____

_____

_____

Question 2:

Consider turnover of top or critical talent in your department or within your team. If there is turnover, are there any discernable trends for why the talent left? If there was low, or no, turnover, what would you consider to be the single greatest factor for retention of top talent? What questions should you be asking yourself in order to develop further insights into retaining talent?

Question 3:
Sometimes we measure retention by the numbers retained. What other factors should you be measuring to ensure that you are retaining the right talent and creating an exit plan for those wrong for the current circumstances?

Synthesizing and Applying Theme:
Consider your entries for this theme. What insights did you gain?
Is there anything you will seek to do more of, differently, or less of
because of your reflection on the topics in this theme?

_____

_____

_____

_____

_____

_____

_____

_____

_____

_____

_____

_____

_____

_____

_____

_____

_____

_____

_____

_____

_____

_____

_____

_____

_____

_____

THEME TEN

Developing Others

What is needed is a deep-rooted conviction, among business unit heads and line leaders that people really matter – that leaders must develop the capabilities of employees, nurture their careers, and manage the performance of individuals and teams.

-Drew Hansen

TOPIC 1

Developing Staff

"Managers also have to challenge employees within their areas of talent, then help them gain the skills and knowledge they need to build their talents into strengths - help employees develop ownership of their goals, targets and milestones so employees can enhance their contributions to the company and increase their impact."

- Curt Coffman

Organizations, leaders, and individuals all have a role responsibility and a stake in professional development. This topic you will examine what your past behavior tells you with regard to how you define and balance each party's role and responsibility in professional development. Further, you will explore your approach for developing the skills and capabilities of those around you.

Question 1:
Consider the membership of your team. How do you know individuals are capitalizing on their strengths? What are you doing to stretch your employees to further develop their own self-identities, competencies, and knowledge?

_____

_____

_____

_____

_____

_____

_____

_____

_____

Question 2:

Think about your own developmental challenges. What are they? Are you actively addressing these challenges and simultaneously modeling the importance of on-going development? How?

_____

_____

_____

_____

_____

_____

_____

_____

_____

_____

_____

_____

_____

_____

_____

_____

_____

_____

_____

_____

_____

_____

_____

_____

_____

Question 3:

Evaluate what, if any, processes you have put in place to recognize and reward staff members who pursue further development opportunities on their own, who commit to mastering or expanding a skill or knowledge area. What should you be doing more of, less of, or differently to reward this desired behavior?

_____

_____

_____

_____

_____

_____

_____

_____

_____

_____

_____

_____

_____

_____

_____

_____

_____

_____

_____

_____

_____

_____

TOPIC 2

Growing Leaders

"Potential leaders make themselves valuable because they see and seize opportunities to better the organization-regardless of the nature or size of the task."

-John Maxwell

Leaders are expected to cultivate other leaders. Great leaders structure the work and the processes around the work to facilitate the emergence and further development of future leaders. This topic you will explore what you believe about developing other leaders and consider ways that you can increase your effectiveness in growing future leaders.

Question 1:

How do you invest in development of potential leaders around you? Do you provide them access to different leaders or participation in different decision-making circles? How should you invest more?

_____

_____

_____

_____

_____

_____

_____

_____

_____

_____

_____

Question 2:

How can you expand the leadership potential of the staff who report to you? Think of ways you can connect them to a leader, to an experience, or to a resource that challenges them to think about the leader they want to be.

Question 3:

If you were to take an extended leave of absence, whom would you designate to do your work? How would they have to be prepared to do your work as effectively as you would like? What can you do now to ensure that you have a growing leader available to cover for you should an unanticipated event arise?

_____

_____

_____

_____

_____

_____

_____

_____

_____

_____

_____

_____

_____

_____

_____

_____

_____

_____

_____

_____

_____

_____

_____

_____

_____

TOPIC 3
Exploring Critical Thinking

"Critical thinking is self-directed, self-disciplined, self-monitored, and self-correcting. It presupposes assent to rigorous standards of excellence and mindful command of their use."
-Richard Paul, Ph.D. & Linda Elder, Ph.D.

Leaders today must model, expect, and even teach critical thinking - a disciplined process for exploring and evaluating information and ideas. In addition, leaders must also model entrepreneurial creativity and a strong drive for innovation.

Question 1:
What mechanisms do you put in place when you are evaluating a decision to ensure that you are not affected by biased, distorted, incomplete, or uniformed thinking?

_____

_____

_____

_____

_____

_____

_____

_____

_____

_____

_____

_____

_____

_____

Question 2:

Consider the following attributes of a critical thinker and evaluate your level of perceived proficiency with each: 1. Raises vital questions and problems and is able to articulate them clearly and accurately. 2. Gathers and analyzes relevant information to come to well-reasoned conclusions and solutions. 3. Tests conclusions against relevant criteria and standards. 4. Has an open mind and a heightened sense of inquiry regarding alternative systems of thought and approaches. 5. Communicates effectively with others to generate effective solutions to complex problems.

_____

_____

_____

_____

_____

_____

_____

_____

_____

_____

_____

_____

_____

_____

_____

_____

_____

_____

_____

_____

Question 3:

Consider how you recruit for critical thinking. What questions should you be asking to ensure that your new hires reflect the level and types of thinking that you require? How can the current system of selection be modified to give proper emphasis to those desired thinking skills and related competencies?

TOPIC 4

Development Initiatives

Our learning is targeted. I am always asking people, 'Are you getting the right learning to do this job?'
-Fred Poses, COO Allied Signal

As a leader, it is your job to ensure that your employee development opportunities are targeted to increasing the knowledge and skills needed for success of the individual(s) and the organization. It is not enough to merely check off a box on a list of mandatory trainings. In this topic, you will reflect on what you are and can do to ensure development initiatives consider where the employee is in terms of knowledge and ability and where you need them to be to be successful in their current job, to take on expanded responsibilities, or to advance to a higher order position.

Question 1:
Reflect on your own learning over the course of your career. What are all the ways in which you acquired new knowledge or new abilities? With regard to your own learning and growth which of these learning experiences served you best?

_____

_____

_____

_____

_____

_____

_____

_____

_____

_____

Question 2:

Reflect on the learning opportunities you have provided to your staff members, individually and collectively? Think about one high performer and one employee who needed to get better at their current job. What factors influenced you when selecting the type of learning opportunities, you would provide in these two very different situations?

_____

_____

_____

_____

_____

_____

_____

_____

_____

_____

_____

_____

_____

_____

_____

_____

_____

_____

_____

_____

_____

_____

_____

Question 3:
Reflect on a time when an employee who was afforded a learning opportunity failed to acquire or apply the new learning? Compare and contrast that example with a time when an employee did acquire and apply the new learning? What do you attribute as the cause for different employee responses to learning?

_____

_____

_____

_____

_____

_____

_____

_____

_____

_____

_____

_____

_____

_____

_____

_____

_____

_____

_____

_____

_____

_____

_____

_____

Synthesizing and Applying Theme:

Consider your entries for this theme. What insights did you gain? Is there anything you will seek to do more of, differently, or less of because of your reflection on the topics in this theme?

_____

_____

_____

_____

_____

_____

_____

_____

_____

_____

_____

_____

_____

_____

_____

_____

_____

_____

_____

_____

_____

_____

THEME ELEVEN
Conflict

The better able team members are to engage, speak, listen, hear, interpret, and respond constructively, the more likely their teams are to leverage conflict rather than be leveled by it.

-Craig E. Runde, J.D. and Tim A. Flanagan

TOPIC 1

Culture of Openness

"Culture is the framework in which we communicate."
-Stephen Roberts

Leaders know that a lack of conflict is not a sign of a healthy organization. Conflict can, when used correctly, be an effective leadership tool for encouraging innovation, avoiding errors of ignorance, and raising the bar on ideas. Consider your own beliefs about conflict and how these beliefs show up in your leadership. What messages about a culture of openness are you sending?

Question 1:
As a leader, what behaviors do you demonstrate that convey to your team that you want to hear their opinions? How do you address your team members' opinions while leading with yours?

_____

_____

_____

_____

_____

_____

_____

_____

_____

_____

_____

_____

_____

_____

Question 2:

What are the situations where you would suppress the opinions of others on your team? What behaviors do you employ? Why do you choose to suppress opinions at such times?

_____

_____

_____

_____

_____

_____

_____

_____

_____

_____

_____

_____

_____

_____

_____

_____

_____

_____

_____

_____

_____

_____

_____

_____

_____

_____

_____

Question 3:

What changes in systems or climate do you believe would ensure that your organization is more open to hearing controversial opinions?

_____

_____

_____

_____

_____

_____

_____

_____

_____

_____

_____

_____

_____

_____

_____

_____

_____

_____

_____

_____

_____

_____

_____

_____

_____

TOPIC 2

Using Conflict to Advance

"Lack of conflict is not the same as real agreement; consensus can be a disguise for disengagement."

-Aneel Karnani, Ph.D.

Through their own actions, leaders tell others whether conflict is encouraged or discouraged and when and if contrary opinions are welcome. This topic you will examine behaviors that you employ to leverage conflict to advance team performance and lead to new solutions.

Question 1:
As the leader how do you actively seek out opposing points of view and encourage debate on negative or contrary opinions?

_____

_____

_____

_____

_____

_____

_____

_____

_____

_____

_____

_____

_____

_____

Question 2:

What have you done, or can you do ensure contrary opinions are shared in a way that directs attention to the issues, solutions, facts, and data rather than in ways that serve only to escalate conflicts between people, values, and opinions?

_____

_____

_____

_____

_____

_____

_____

_____

_____

_____

_____

_____

_____

_____

_____

_____

_____

_____

_____

_____

_____

_____

_____

Question 3:

What efforts have you made or seen other leaders make to ensure a diversity of thought and perspective so as to generate robust dialogue rather than succumb to group think?

_____

_____

_____

_____

_____

_____

_____

_____

_____

_____

_____

_____

_____

_____

_____

_____

_____

_____

_____

_____

_____

_____

_____

_____

_____

TOPIC 3

Conflict Communications

"The void created by the failure to communicate is soon filled with poison, drivel and misrepresentation."

-C. Northcote Parkinson, Ph.D.

Leaders cannot afford to avoid difficult conversations. They must be prepared to talk about difference in opinion, missed expectations, change, and any number of other emotionally laden topics. This topic you will think about difficult conversations you have had in the past and how you performed.

Question 1:
What makes a conversation difficult for you? Explore this question as it relates to conversations with staff, colleagues, and supervisors. Are there any themes among the three categories of workplace staff?

_____

_____

_____

_____

_____

_____

_____

_____

_____

_____

_____

_____

Question 2:

Think about a time when, in the middle of a conflict, you acted in ways or said things that escalated the conflict? In retrospect what could you have done or said that would have led to a quicker and better resolution rather than to more conflict?

_____

_____

_____

_____

_____

_____

_____

_____

_____

_____

_____

_____

_____

_____

_____

_____

_____

_____

_____

_____

_____

_____

Question 3:

Consider a time when someone expressed to you that they felt you were unfair or unreasonable? How did you respond to the person? What, if anything, would you do differently if you had the opportunity?

_____

_____

_____

_____

_____

_____

_____

_____

_____

_____

_____

_____

_____

_____

_____

_____

_____

_____

_____

_____

_____

_____

_____

_____

_____

_____

TOPIC 4

Conflict & Stress

"The ability to summon positive emotions during periods of intense stress lies at the heart of effective leadership."

-Jim Loehr, Ph.D.

The work of a leader is constantly changing and often stressful. How you moderate your behavior during times of stress is a hallmark of your leader effectiveness. This topic you will reflect on periods when stress was significant and what you learned from those experiences.

Question 1:

Consider a time when you were under a tremendous amount of stress. How did this stress play out in your attitudes and behaviors at work? What impact did it have on your work performance and your relationships? What did you do to address the impact after the period abated?

_____

_____

_____

_____

_____

_____

_____

_____

_____

_____

_____

_____

_____

Question 2:

What strategies do you use to manage stress? Do you believe others see you as effectively managing your stress and not projecting it upon them? If not, why not? What do you need to do to change this perception if, in fact, it exists?

_____

_____

_____

_____

_____

_____

_____

_____

_____

_____

_____

_____

_____

_____

_____

_____

_____

_____

_____

_____

_____

_____

_____

_____

_____

Question 3:

Identify two or three methods that you use to monitor the stress of those around you. When you see signs of an undue amount of stress in others (be it staff, peers, or supervisors), what do you typically do? What do you think you should do more of or differently in these situations?

Synthesizing and Applying Theme:
Consider your entries for this theme. What insights did you gain?
Is there anything you will seek to do more of, differently, or less of
because of your reflection on the topics in this theme?

_____

_____

_____

_____

_____

_____

_____

_____

_____

_____

_____

_____

_____

_____

_____

_____

_____

_____

_____

THEME TWELVE
Change

Your success in life isn't based on your ability to simply change. It is based on your ability to change faster than your competition, customers, and business.

-Mark Sanborn

TOPIC 1

Inspiring Passion for Change

*"Passion kept one fully in the present, so that time became
a series of mutually exclusive 'nows.'"*

-Sue Halpern

Change begins with passion — passion for what could be. For this
topic, you will explore methods for creating and retaining the spark
needed to motivate and mobilize through a change initiative.

Question 1:
What makes you passionate about your organization? How can
you use your passion to drive growth? How can your colleagues
use their passion to drive growth?

_____

_____

_____

_____

_____

_____

_____

_____

_____

_____

_____

_____

_____

_____

_____

_____

Question 2:

Describe a time when you were more passionate than others about a new goal, project, or service. What, if anything, did you do to try and facilitate greater passion among others? What would you do differently?

_____

_____

_____

_____

_____

_____

_____

_____

_____

_____

_____

_____

_____

_____

_____

_____

_____

_____

_____

_____

_____

_____

_____

Question 3:
Describe a time when you were feeling less passionate and connected around a new work assignment or project. What behaviors were evident? What, if anything, did you do to find a connection? What do you do when you just cannot generate passion around a new idea or direction?

_____

_____

_____

_____

_____

_____

_____

_____

_____

_____

_____

_____

_____

_____

_____

_____

_____

_____

_____

_____

_____

_____

TOPIC 2

Leading Change

*"People's minds are changed through observation
and not through argument."*

-Will Rogers

Managers, whose focus is today's efficiency, may seek to control, constrain, or otherwise restrict change. Leaders, whose focus is future relevancy and effectiveness, know that change – inspired and well led – is essential for organizational survival. This topic you will explore how you have led change initiatives in the past and the lessons learned from these experiences.

Question 1:
Think about a time when you had to lead others through a significant change in course or direction. What did you do? How did others respond? What did you learn from that experience?

_____

_____

_____

_____

_____

_____

_____

_____

_____

_____

_____

_____

_____

Question 2:
Think about a prior initiative that you led that was not successful. Describe the situation. What did you do (or not do) that led to the lack of success? What adaptations could you or others have made to create a different outcome?

_____

_____

_____

_____

_____

_____

_____

_____

_____

_____

_____

_____

_____

_____

_____

_____

_____

_____

_____

_____

_____

_____

_____

Question 3:
Think about a process or system that you either adapted or assisted others in adapting for greater efficiencies in cost and time or other favorable outputs. What lessons from this experience are transferrable to your current work environment? What other questions do you need to ask yourself about the effectiveness of your role in fostering adaptability within your team?

_____

_____

_____

_____

_____

_____

_____

_____

_____

_____

_____

_____

_____

_____

_____

_____

_____

_____

_____

_____

_____

TOPIC 3

Learning from Change

"When we are no longer able to change a situation, we are challenged to change ourselves."

-Victor Frankl, M.D.

Change is inevitable in the life of a leader; especially one who takes risks, innovates, and pushes beyond boundaries. Effective leaders also find the learning opportunity in every change. This topic, you will reflect on prior changes that helped you to make critical future corrections in your process or approach.

Question 1:
Think about a change from early in your leadership experience. What happened and how did you handle it? What did you learn?

_____

_____

_____

_____

_____

_____

_____

_____

_____

_____

_____

_____

_____

Question 2:

If you had the opportunity to change one leadership decision that you have made in your career, what would it be? What did you learn from the impact of that decision on others, on the task/problem, or the organization?

_____

_____

_____

_____

_____

_____

_____

_____

_____

_____

_____

_____

_____

_____

_____

_____

_____

_____

_____

_____

_____

_____

_____

_____

Question 3:

Look back and compare your organization today with that of several years ago. What did the organization have to learn in order to change? What have those changes meant for how you operate as a leader in that organization?

_____

_____

_____

_____

_____

_____

_____

_____

_____

_____

_____

_____

_____

_____

_____

_____

_____

_____

_____

_____

_____

_____

_____

_____

TOPIC 4

Defining Change

"Leaders establish the vision for the future and set the strategy for getting there; they cause change. They motivate and inspire others to go in the right direction and they, along with everyone else, sacrifice to get there."

Leo Buscaglia, Ph.D.

The hallmark of a seasoned leader is to define change as an inevitable condition of the work environment and to use the change to mobilize, create, and motivate. This topic, you will consider areas in your current role where you need to articulate a needed change. You will also explore behaviors that you should continue to refine or develop to help others manage transitions.

Question 1:
Think about an area that you are responsible for that could benefit from a significant change. What do you want the end result to look like? How are you going to manage the transition?

_____

_____

_____

_____

_____

_____

_____

_____

_____

_____

_____

_____

_____

Question 2:

Consider a time when you were the first to identify and define a change that, if implemented, would significantly contribute to success. What did you do? Why was the change critical? How did you help others understand its urgency?

_____

_____

_____

_____

_____

_____

_____

_____

_____

_____

_____

_____

_____

_____

_____

_____

_____

_____

_____

_____

_____

_____

_____

Question 3:

What could you do in your work setting to reframe the concept of change? Consider leaders who have used change as a galvanizing and motivating force in their work. What did they say or do that made the prospect of change seem more exciting and less daunting? What can you take from those lessons and apply in your leadership role?

_____

_____

_____

_____

_____

_____

_____

_____

_____

_____

_____

_____

_____

_____

_____

_____

_____

_____

_____

_____

_____

_____

Synthesizing and Applying Theme:
Consider your entries for this theme. What insights did you gain?
Is there anything you will seek to do more of, differently, or less of
because of your reflection on the topics in this theme?

_____

_____

_____

_____

_____

_____

_____

_____

_____

_____

_____

_____

_____

_____

_____

_____

_____

_____

_____

_____

_____

_____

_____

_____

_____

_____

THEME THIRTEEN
Strategy

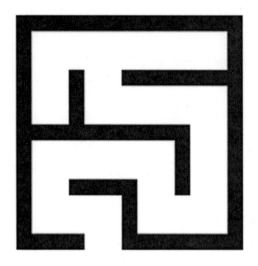

The essence of strategy is to make controversial choices in order to gain a competitive advantage.

–Aneel Karnani, Ph.D.

TOPIC 1

Strategic Understanding

"However beautiful the strategy, you should occasionally look at the results."

-Winston Churchill

The meta competency of awareness requires not only that you are aware of yourself and others, but also that you have an awareness, an understanding of the culture and context within which you are leading. This topic you will reflect on questions that address that context awareness so that you might reduce the uncertainty.

Question 1:
What questions have you asked, or seen other leaders ask to confirm or choose the arena(s) in which your current organization does and should operate? What kind of insights do these questions provide?

_____

_____

_____

_____

_____

_____

_____

_____

_____

_____

_____

_____

_____

_____

Question 2:

When you join a new team or organization how do you determine your competitive advantage and the value proposition you seek to offer the greater organization and/or your external customers? What people or groups of people do you speak with? What materials do you look at?

_____

_____

_____

_____

_____

_____

_____

_____

_____

_____

_____

_____

_____

_____

_____

_____

_____

_____

_____

_____

_____

_____

_____

_____

Question 3:

What questions have you asked, or seen other leaders ask to ascertain the capacity of your current team or organization to carry out the strategies you are contemplating?

_____

_____

_____

_____

_____

_____

_____

_____

_____

_____

_____

_____

_____

_____

_____

_____

_____

_____

_____

_____

_____

_____

_____

_____

_____

TOPIC 2

Strategic Process

"When I have one topic to solve a seemingly impossible problem, I spend six days defining the problem. Then, the solution becomes obvious."

-Albert Einstein, Ph.D.

Leaders know that the best visions of what could be are only as good as the roadmap developed to get there. This topic you will explore how you identify strategic priorities and your process for developing and evaluating strategy.

Question 1:
How do you currently identify your strategic priorities? How do you anticipate the execution opportunities and challenges inherent in those strategies? What do you need to adjust or incorporate into your planning process to ensure you are designing strategies that designed to be executed?

_____

_____

_____

_____

_____

_____

_____

_____

_____

_____

_____

_____

Question 2:

What is your process for developing and evaluating strategy? What do you do (or should you do) to ensure that people, systems, and strategy are seamlessly linked together?

_____

_____

_____

_____

_____

_____

_____

_____

_____

_____

_____

_____

_____

_____

_____

_____

_____

_____

_____

_____

_____

_____

_____

_____

Question 3:

If you were to grade yourself and your current team on the effectiveness of strategic planning and execution efforts, what grade would be assigned? What would have to happen to improve this grade if, indeed, there is room for improvement?

_____

_____

_____

_____

_____

_____

_____

_____

_____

_____

_____

_____

_____

_____

_____

_____

_____

_____

_____

_____

_____

_____

_____

_____

_____

TOPIC 3

Exploring Opportunities

"We are continually faced by great opportunities brilliantly disguised as insoluble problems."

-Lee Iacocca

Great leaders and great companies miss revolutionary opportunities. Kodak is a frequently cited example for having passed on electrophotography (xerography) that birthed Xerox and later, the digital camera movement that led to its bankruptcy. This topic you will examine those behaviors that you do, or should be doing, to explore those untapped opportunities all around you.

Question 1:
Think about the last great idea that you remember having. What prompted your breakthrough in thinking? How can you channel it again?

_____

_____

_____

_____

_____

_____

_____

_____

_____

_____

_____

_____

_____

Question 2:

What are some of the disruptive technologies facing your organization? What are you doing in response?

Question 3:

Evaluate the current practices you engage in (or identify some practices you should begin) to identify and track opportunities for your organization.

_____

_____

_____

_____

_____

_____

_____

_____

_____

_____

_____

_____

_____

_____

_____

_____

_____

_____

_____

_____

_____

_____

_____

_____

TOPIC 4

Setting Strategic Priorities

"The essence of strategy is choosing what not to do."

-Michael E. Porter, Ph.D.

Strategy is often revealed through risk taking, controversy, and an almost hostile rejection of the status quo. Good leaders can leverage these forces for greater strategic advantage. This topic you will explore how to foster environments that facilitate strategic focus and intent.

Question 1:

What are your strategic priorities? How do you know they are the right ones?

_____

_____

_____

_____

_____

_____

_____

_____

_____

_____

_____

_____

_____

_____

_____

Question 2:

What types of strategic boundaries have you set for your organization or your team? How do you balance these boundaries without compromising agility and innovation?

_____

_____

_____

_____

_____

_____

_____

_____

_____

_____

_____

_____

_____

_____

_____

_____

_____

_____

_____

_____

_____

_____

_____

Question 3:

Examine your process for keeping your strategy robust and relevant. What indicators do you monitor for knowing when to stop, start or change an approach?

Synthesizing and Applying Theme:

Consider your entries for this theme. What insights did you gain? Is there anything you will seek to do more of, differently, or less of because of your reflection on the topics in this theme?

_____

_____

_____

_____

_____

_____

_____

_____

_____

_____

_____

_____

_____

_____

_____

_____

_____

_____

_____

_____

_____

_____

_____

_____

_____

_____

_____

THEME FOURTEEN

Sustaining Forward Momentum

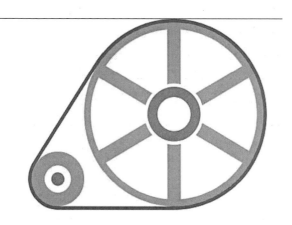

If you don't know how to execute, the whole of your efforts as a leader will always be less than the sum of its parts.

-Larry Bossidy & Ram Charan, Ph.D.

TOPIC 1

Creating Winning Streaks

"Winning streaks are empowering. People feel in control of their game, and, in turn, they are more likely to be handed control. An expectation of continued winning gives decision makers and resource allocators confidence that people can handle responsibility, deserve to know the facts, attract the best talent, benefit from training, pull together a group without depending excessively on stars - and produce those wins."

-Rosabeth Moss Kanter, Ph.D.

Great leaders have a knack for orchestrating a series of winning streaks—keeping momentum going through a series of big and small wins. This topic you will examine your behaviors that facilitate a winning culture and a flywheel of forward momentum.

Question 1:
What processes have you established (or should you establish) in your team setting to monitor for the presence of the pathologies that can inhibit winning streaks (e.g., decreased communication, increased blame, focus turns inward, etc.)?

_____

_____

_____

_____

_____

_____

_____

_____

_____

Question 2:

Consider what behaviors you are rewarding in your team. Are you rewarding individual contributions, collaborative efforts, or both? Are you rewarding those behaviors that lead to winning streaks such as good communication, collaboration, innovative thinking, and appropriate risk-taking? What should you do differently if anything, to accelerate the flywheel of success?

_____

_____

_____

_____

_____

_____

_____

_____

_____

_____

_____

_____

_____

_____

_____

_____

_____

_____

_____

_____

_____

_____

Question 3:
Think about a time you were part of a losing streak. What happened (or did not happen) to turn the losing streak around? In hindsight, what would you do differently now?

_____

_____

_____

_____

_____

_____

_____

_____

_____

_____

_____

_____

_____

_____

_____

_____

_____

_____

_____

_____

_____

_____

_____

_____

_____

TOPIC 2

Ensuring Accountability

"There can be no true response without responsibility; there can be no responsibility without response."

-Arthur Vogel

At the end of the day, leaders are not measured on their vision or strategy but on their ability to get the right things done well. Think about what successful leaders do, what you do, and what you must start or keep doing in order to get things done.

Question 1:

What behaviors do you consistently display with peers and team members that convey that you are accountable for your assignments and results? Are there any areas where you could improve your accountability? If so, how could you go about making those changes?

_____

_____

_____

_____

_____

_____

_____

_____

_____

_____

_____

Question 2:

Consider ways that you convey and ensure accountability among your team. What are some behaviors that you consistently demonstrate to your staff that communicates that accountability for results is critical? What additional changes could be made to make expectations clearer?

_____

_____

_____

_____

_____

_____

_____

_____

_____

_____

_____

_____

_____

_____

_____

_____

_____

_____

_____

_____

_____

_____

Question 3:

Consider how (or if) you recognize and reward individuals who assume accountability for more than what is required by their job descriptions—when they decided on their own that something needed to be done and they did it. What do you (or should you) consistently do to reinforce this behavior?

_____

_____

_____

_____

_____

_____

_____

_____

_____

_____

_____

_____

_____

_____

_____

_____

_____

_____

_____

_____

_____

_____

_____

TOPIC 3

Execution Discipline

"Leaders in an execution culture design strategies that are more road maps than rigid paths enshrined in fat planning books. That way they can respond quickly when the unexpected happens. Their strategies are designed to be executed."

-Larry Bossidy & Ram Charan, Ph.D.

Effective execution starts with disciplined thoughts, disciplined people, and disciplined action. Great leaders see execution as a discipline and central to strategy. This topic you will examine behaviors that facilitate effective execution.

Question 1:

Think about a time when you missed a deadline or failed to successfully execute a task for which you were responsible. What did you do to right the situation? What would you do differently today?

_____

_____

_____

_____

_____

_____

_____

_____

_____

_____

_____

_____

_____

Question 2:

What systems and processes do you use (or should us) to keep execution expectations and priorities in the forefront of your organization's or team's efforts? What do you do when focus slips from results?

_____

_____

_____

_____

_____

_____

_____

_____

_____

_____

_____

_____

_____

_____

_____

_____

_____

_____

_____

_____

_____

_____

_____

_____

Question 3:

Think about an execution strategy that required change in the middle due to unexpected conditions or variables. How did you adapt the strategy while keeping the focus on accountability?

_____

_____

_____

_____

_____

_____

_____

_____

_____

_____

_____

_____

_____

_____

_____

_____

_____

_____

_____

_____

_____

_____

_____

_____

_____

TOPIC 4

Communicating Results

"The two words information and communication are often used interchangeably, but they signify quite different things. Information is giving out; communication is getting through."
- Sydney Harris

Communicating progress, particularly during the execution of a critical project, is a central leadership activity. Often communication is compromised by competing priorities, constant change, the "next thing," and daily operational demands. Leaders may have the best intention to share, but often overlook or shortchange this critical activity. This topic you will examine your behaviors for ensuring consistent and clear communication.

Question 1:
Think about a time you were accused of not sharing critical information (or the right amount of it). What were the reasons? What were the consequences? Would you do anything differently today?

_____

_____

_____

_____

_____

_____

_____

_____

_____

_____

_____

_____

Question 2:

What criteria do you use when determining what information to share with your team, your boss, and your peers. Are the criteria different for each of the intended audiences? If so, why?

_____

_____

_____

_____

_____

_____

_____

_____

_____

_____

_____

_____

_____

_____

_____

_____

_____

_____

_____

_____

_____

_____

_____

_____

_____

_____

Question 3:
What are other methods that you could employ to better communicate project progress and results to stakeholders. What one thing could you begin to do today that could enhance your reputation as a communicator as opposed to an information giver?

_____

_____

_____

_____

_____

_____

_____

_____

_____

_____

_____

_____

_____

_____

_____

_____

_____

_____

_____

_____

_____

_____

Synthesizing and Applying Theme:

Consider your entries for this theme. What insights did you gain? Is there anything you will seek to do more of, differently, or less of because of your reflection on the topics in this theme?

_____

_____

_____

_____

_____

_____

_____

_____

_____

_____

_____

_____

_____

_____

_____

_____

_____

_____

_____

_____

_____

_____

_____

_____

_____

_____

_____

THEME FIFTEEN
Connected Communications

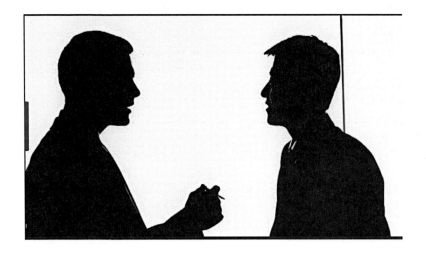

I believe we can change the world if we just start talking

to one another again.

-Margaret Wheatley, Ph.D.

TOPIC 1

Connecting for Influence

Change happens by listening and then starting a dialogue with the people who are doing something you don't believe is right.

-Jane Goodall, Ph.D.

We have our greatest influence when we are willing to balance our need to advocate for our starting own beliefs with time spent inquiring about the starting beliefs of the other party. In this topic, you will reflect on what you have done, and can do to increase your influence by increasing your listening to and observing others.

Question 1:
Consider a time when you sought to influence another to change their decision or behavior but you were ineffective. Next consider a time when you sought to influence another to change their decision or behavior and you were successful. Compare and contrast these two conversations and the status of your relationship with the other person following the conversation.

_____

_____

_____

_____

_____

_____

_____

_____

_____

_____

_____

_____

_____

Question 2:

Returning to the examples you considered in Question 1. Reflect on what you learned about the other person's true interests (what they really wanted not just their stated position) over the course of the conversation. How did, could or should that knowledge influence your approach to the conversation or even your own beliefs about the position you had taken at the start of the conversation.

_____

_____

_____

_____

_____

_____

_____

_____

_____

_____

_____

_____

_____

_____

_____

_____

_____

_____

_____

_____

_____

_____

_____

Question 3:

Think about a time when you wanted another person to take a specific action and you believed you did not have time to listen to their perspective.   What were the short-term and long-term consequences of failing to take the time to listen?   On the accomplishment of the task? On future performance? On your future relationship with the other person?

_____

_____

_____

_____

_____

_____

_____

_____

_____

_____

_____

_____

_____

_____

_____

_____

_____

_____

_____

_____

_____

_____

_____

_____

TOPIC 2

Consequences of Distrust

"Our distrust is expensive."
-Ralph Waldo Emerson

Before people will be open and honest with each other there must be trust. To earn trust and to gain followers, you must be prepared for a stakeholder scrutiny that demands transparency, integrity, and ethics. Without trust in their leaders, individuals may comply but will never commit. Without trust in their leaders, teams may finish but will never excel. Without trust in their leaders, organizations may survive but will not thrive. During this theme, you will explore personal and institutional trust, integrity and character and their critical role in your leadership effectiveness.

Question 1:
Consider behaviors and characteristics you have observed from others that convey a lack of personal integrity and character. What is it about these behaviors and characteristics that diminish trust?

_____

_____

_____

_____

_____

_____

_____

_____

_____

_____

_____

_____

Question 2:

Think about a time when a supervisor, co-worker, or staff member lost your trust. What did they do or say that compromised this trust? Was the relationship ultimately restored? If not, why? If yes, what had to occur to bring the restoration?

_____

_____

_____

_____

_____

_____

_____

_____

_____

_____

_____

_____

_____

_____

_____

_____

_____

_____

_____

_____

_____

_____

_____

_____

Question 3:

Think about a time when you said or did something (or failed to do or say something) that resulted in diminished trust by others. Why did the behavior have this impact? How did this experience change your later behaviors? What would you do differently today if faced with the same circumstances?

_____

_____

_____

_____

_____

_____

_____

_____

_____

_____

_____

_____

_____

_____

_____

_____

_____

_____

_____

_____

_____

_____

_____

_____

TOPIC 3:

Trust and Communications

*"The only way to build trust professionally or personally
Is by being trustworthy."*

-Gerald Arpey

As a leader, what you model, what you allow, and what you do not allow all combine in ways that mold the character of your team and your area of responsibility. Explore the behaviors that you demonstrate to invite the unpopular opinion, the sharing of (sometimes brutal) truth, handling breaches of ethics in your work team and leaving a legacy of integrity.

Question 1:
Consider what you do, or have observed other leaders do, that make it safe for people to share contrary opinions, brutal facts and even challenge the ethics or values behind a decision. What more can you do to ensure people know that they are expected to speak the truth and protected and even validated for doing so?

_____

_____

_____

_____

_____

_____

_____

_____

_____

_____

_____

_____

Question 2:

Consider what more you can do to hold your group accountable for helping to ensure a trustful workplace. Consider what staff members are currently being told (or should be told) about ethical expectations when they join your team and how these expectations are routinely revisited. Consider all of the ways and places that you can reinforce the values and ethical standards that you expect your team to demonstrate.

_____

_____

_____

_____

_____

_____

_____

_____

_____

_____

_____

_____

_____

_____

_____

_____

_____

_____

_____

_____

_____

_____

_____

Question 3:

Consider what you would do as a team leader or as a team member should one of your team members violate an ethical principle. Are the steps clearly established? Does everyone share the same understanding about what is appropriate, allowable, ethical, and reasonable? If not, what can you do to ensure their shared understanding?

_____

_____

_____

_____

_____

_____

_____

_____

_____

_____

_____

_____

_____

_____

_____

_____

_____

_____

_____

_____

_____

_____

_____

_____

_____

TOPIC 4:

Fears and Barriers to Connected Communications

The void created by the failure to communicate is soon filled with poison, drivel, and misrepresentation.

C. Northcote Parkinson, Ph.D.

When we fail to have authentic conversations, we miss opportunities to influence each other, resolve differences, solve problems, better understand each other's perspective, collaborate effectively, innovate, or improve matters, or move from being reactive to proactive. In this topic, you will consider how your fears and barriers are keeping you from having these important conversations.

Question 1:
Think about a conversation you anticipate will be difficult and so you have delayed or otherwise avoided the conversation? What fears or barriers are keeping you from having that conversation? Related to your beliefs about your own skills as a communicator or the other party's skills as a communicator? Related to your current or future relationship with the other party?

_____

_____

_____

_____

_____

_____

_____

_____

Question 2:

Reflect on a difficult conversation you failed to have? What were the consequences, positive or negative, of avoiding that conversation? For you personally? For the other person? For your relationship? For your team? For your organization? For your customers or clients?

_____

_____

_____

_____

_____

_____

_____

_____

_____

_____

_____

_____

_____

_____

_____

_____

_____

_____

_____

_____

_____

_____

_____

_____

Question 3:

Returning to the conversation you considered in Question 2, reflect on the potential benefits that could result if you were able to effectively connect and communicate with the other person on the matter at hand. For you personally? For the other person? For your relationship? For your team? For your organization? For your customers or clients?

_____

_____

_____

_____

_____

_____

_____

_____

_____

_____

_____

_____

_____

_____

_____

_____

_____

_____

_____

_____

_____

_____

_____

Synthesizing and Applying Theme:
Consider your entries for this theme. What insights did you gain?
Is there anything you will seek to do more of, differently, or less of
because of your reflection on the topics in this theme?

_____

_____

_____

_____

_____

_____

_____

_____

_____

_____

_____

_____

_____

_____

_____

_____

_____

_____

_____

_____

_____

_____

_____

_____